SIMON JEWISH MUSIC SERIES

Level 1

Marcy Rubin
Arranged by Avremi G
Designed by VannInnovation

This Series is dedicated to my father and teacher,
Ronald Simon z"l
He took the time to teach me piano & taught me that music is
something that should be part of your life every day.

*Thank you to Aaron Simon for your guidance and assistance
with this book from beginning to end.*

Ki Va Moed and Eso Enai © unknown & 1959 Rabbi Shlomo Carlebach, BMI.
Printed with permission of the Estate of Rabbi Shlomo Carlebach
For further information: neshamacarlebach@gmail.com
These arrangements © Copyright 2020 Toccata Method® LLC.
All Rights Reserved   Used by permission

ISBN # 978-1-7333103-5-2

toccata
method®

NOTE TO TEACHERS

My students have often asked for Jewish music when they are learning to play the piano but there has been a void in quality performance books in this area. Students that play music that they know and enjoy progress faster and stay interested. We compiled the Simon Jewish Music Series to give children quality music to practice while they're learning to play.

Each song has two pages. The page on the left is the accompaniment and the page on the right is the Level 1 song. The accompaniment can be played by the teacher or another student with more experience. It is also designed so that the student can return to the Level 1 book at a later date and play the accompaniment, providing even more value as they advance their skills. The accompaniment is also useful because it provides the student rhythm practice while making the songs more enjoyable to play.

The songs in the beginning of the book are easier and then progress in difficulty. The first song in the Book, "Shabbat Shalom", is a C major scale warm up. It can be used each day as the warm up before practicing. The last song of the book is the challenge song, "Asher Boro". Prior to this song, we have included some finger exercises to prepare the student for performing this piece. The students should practice these combinations and then begin playing the music after learning them.

We hope you will enjoy playing the music in this book as much as I enjoyed creating it.

Marcy Rubin & the Simonland Music Team

LOOK FOR OUR OTHER MUSIC BOOKS IN THE SIMON JEWISH MUSIC SERIES:

Simon Jewish Music Series Jewish Songbook for Piano Level 2

Simon Jewish Music Series Jewish Songbook for Piano Level 3

Simon Jewish Music Series Jewish Songbook for Piano Level 4

Simon Jewish Music Series Jewish Songbook for Piano Level 5

Simon Jewish Music Series Jewish Songbook for Piano Level 6

Also coming soon:
The Toccata Method learning System and Dry Erase Board.

DEAR STUDENTS,

We created this series of books so you can learn piano by playing fun, enjoyable Jewish music. You can play each song on its own to start. These songs also have accompaniments, so you can play them as a duet with a friend, a teacher, or someone in your family who also likes piano.

Playing these songs should help you become a better piano player and have fun while you do it!

Marcy Rubin
& the Simonland Music Team

TABLE OF CONTENTS

PIANO NOTATION

TIME SIGNATURES

3 Top number (3) means 3 counts in each measure.
4 Bottom number (4) means the quarter note gets 1 beat.

TEMPO

Andante Relaxed slow tempo (73-77 BPM)
Moderato Moderate tempo (86-97 BPM)
Allegro Quick tempo (109-132 BPM)

DYNAMICS

mp **Mezzo Piano** Medium soft
mf **Mezzo Forte** Medium loud
p **Piano** Soft
f **Forte** Loud

NOTATION

Slur 2 notes played smoothly in a row
Tie 2 notes played together as a single note
Repeat Sign Repeat back one time to the previous repeat sign.

THEORY

A semitone is a half step on the piano. A half step is moving from one piano key to the black or white key directly next to it.

Minor second 1 semitone
Major second 2 semitones
Minor third 3 semitones
Major third 4 semitones
Perfect fourth 5 semitones
Perfect fifth 7 semitones

♯ Sharps half step to the right
♭ Flats half step to the left

SCALES

T Tonic: First note of the scale
W Whole step
H Half step
Major Scale Constructed with T W W H W W W H
Natural Minor Scale Constructed with T W H W W H W W
Harmonic Minor Scale Natural Minor Scale with the seventh note raised one semitone
Pick up note First measure of the song has less beats per measure than in the time signature, the remaining beats are in the last measure of the song.

ACCOMPANIMENT

PROGRESS CHART	BEGINNING	PROGRESSING	MASTERED
STUDENT LEVEL 1			
ACCOMPANIMENT LEVEL 2			

Level 2

This Level 2 accompaniment can be played by the teacher or another student. Additionally, the student can return to this book at a later time and play it when they reach the appropriate skill level.

SHABBAT SHALOM

STUDENT PLAYS TWO OCTAVES HIGHER

ANDANTE

Composed by Avremi G.

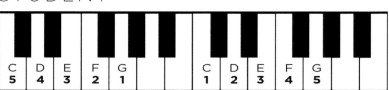

C Major Scale

This song can be used as a finger exercise before practice.

Play this song Andante with a relaxed slow tempo (73-77 BPM).

SHABBAT SHALOM

ANDANTE

Composed by Avremi G.
Lyrics by Aba R.

DAY OF REST IS HERE PUT A - WAY YOUR WORK

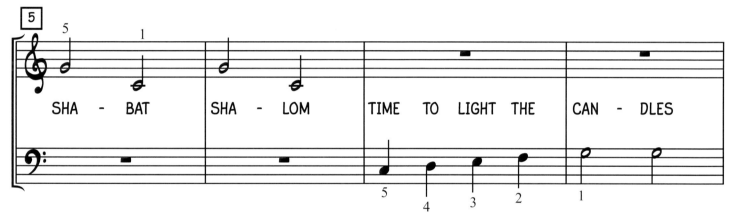

SHA - BAT SHA - LOM TIME TO LIGHT THE CAN - DLES

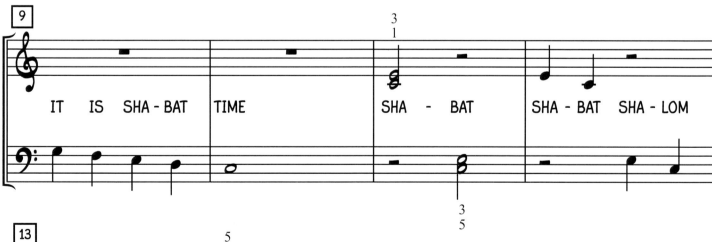

IT IS SHA - BAT TIME SHA - BAT SHA - BAT SHA - LOM

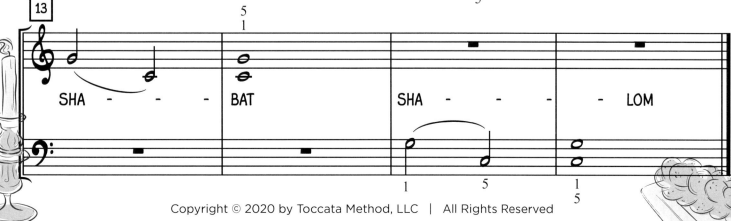

SHA - - - BAT SHA - - - LOM

3

ACCOMPANIMENT

PROGRESS CHART	BEGINNING	PROGRESSING	MASTERED
STUDENT LEVEL 1			
ACCOMPANIMENT LEVEL 3			

Level 3

This Level 3 accompaniment when played with "Shema" is a good way for the student to improve rhythm skills.

SHEMA

STUDENT PLAYS TWO OCTAVES HIGHER

MODERATO

Composed by Avremi G.

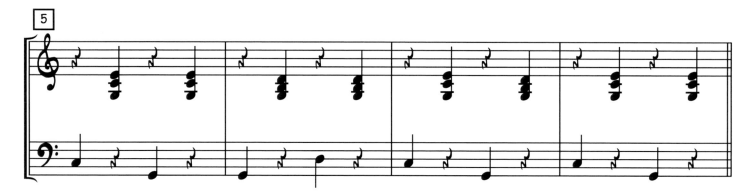

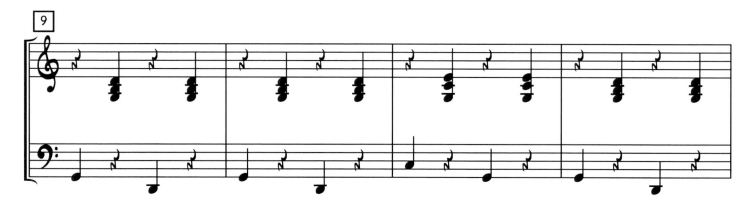

Moderato

Play this song moderato with a moderate tempo, 86-97 BPM.

SHEMA

MODERATO

Composed by Avremi G.
Lyrics by Gabe Simon

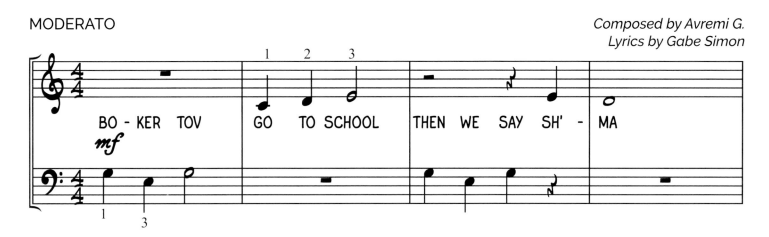

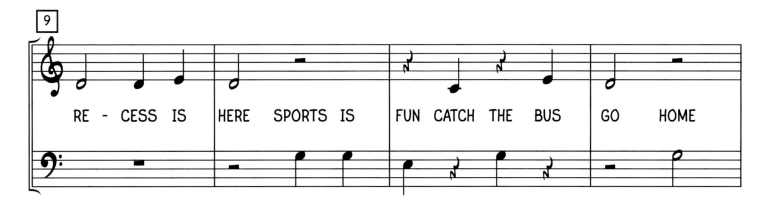

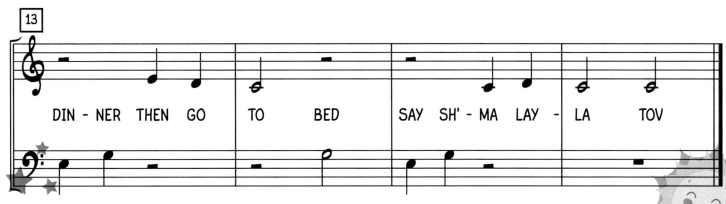

ACCOMPANIMENT

PROGRESS CHART	BEGINNING	PROGRESSING	MASTERED
STUDENT LEVEL 1			
ACCOMPANIMENT LEVEL 2			

Level 2

Ki Va Moed adds the concept of
first and second ending.

KI VA MOED

STUDENT PLAYS TWO OCTAVES HIGHER

Arranged by Avremi G.
Composed by R' Shlomo Carlebach

MODERATO

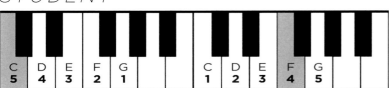

Repeat Sign

Play the Treble Clef F with the fourth finger of your right hand.
Repeat Sign **‖:** Repeat the first and second line twice, between the repeat signs.

KI VA MOED

MODERATO

Arranged by Avremi G.
Composed by R' Shlomo Carlebach

ACCOMPANIMENT

PROGRESS CHART	BEGINNING	PROGRESSING	MASTERED
STUDENT LEVEL 1			
ACCOMPANIMENT LEVEL 3			

Level 3

Student can practice playing thirds and chords in this Level 3 accompaniment.

ESO EINAI

STUDENT PLAYS TWO OCTAVES HIGHER

MODERATO

Arranged by Avremi G.
Composed by R' Shlomo Carlebach

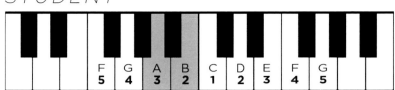

Slur

Play C D E F smoothly in a row in measure 9 of this song.

ESO EINAI

MODERATO

Arranged by Avremi G.
Composed by R' Shlomo Carlebach

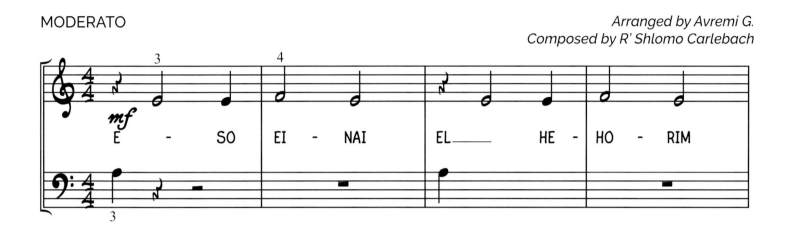

E - SO   EI - NAI   EL____ HE - HO - RIM

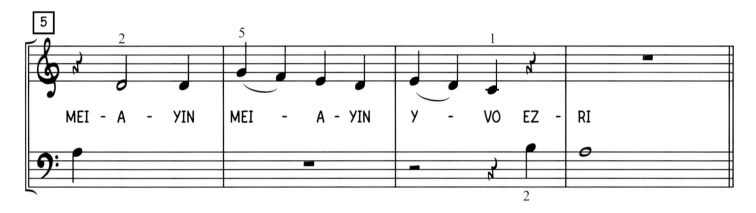

MEI - A - YIN   MEI - A - YIN   Y - VO   EZ - RI

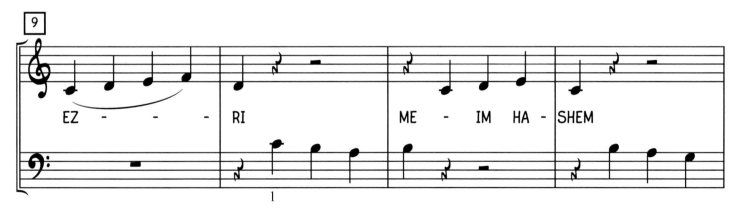

EZ - - - RI   ME - IM HA - SHEM

O - - - SEI   SHO - MA - YIM VO - O - RETZ

PROGRESS CHART	BEGINNING	PROGRESSING	MASTERED
STUDENT LEVEL 1			
ACCOMPANIMENT LEVEL 4			

Level 4

Using this Level 4 accompaniment with the student
is a fun way to improve rhythm skills.

I HAVE A LITTLE DREIDEL

STUDENT PLAYS TWO OCTAVES HIGHER

MODERATO

Arranged by Avremi G.

Treble Clef G

Treble Clef G is added with the fifth finger of the right hand in this song.

I HAVE A LITTLE DREIDEL

MODERATO

Arranged by Avremi G.

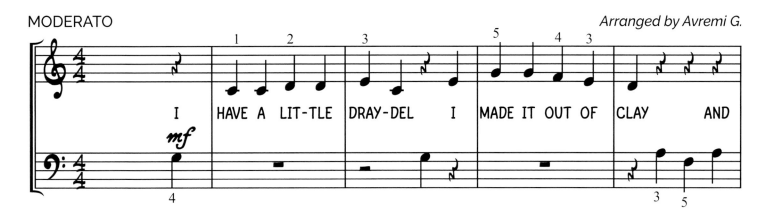

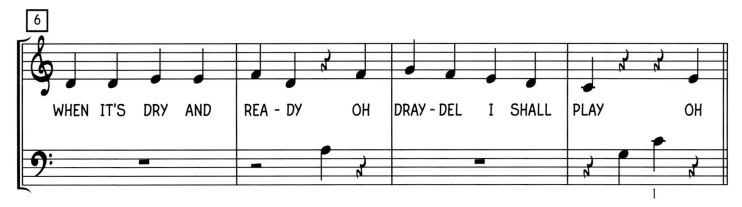

15

ACCOMPANIMENT

PROGRESS CHART	BEGINNING	PROGRESSING	MASTERED
STUDENT LEVEL 1			
ACCOMPANIMENT LEVEL 2			

Level 2

This song is played moderato. Moderato is played at a moderate pace, 98-112 bpm.

WE WANT MOSHIACH NOW

STUDENT PLAYS TWO OCTAVES HIGHER

Arranged by Avremi G.

MODERATO

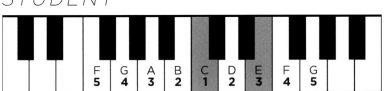

Major Third

Practice playing C and E with your first and third finger of your right hand.

WE WANT MOSHIACH NOW

MODERATO

Arranged by Avremi G.

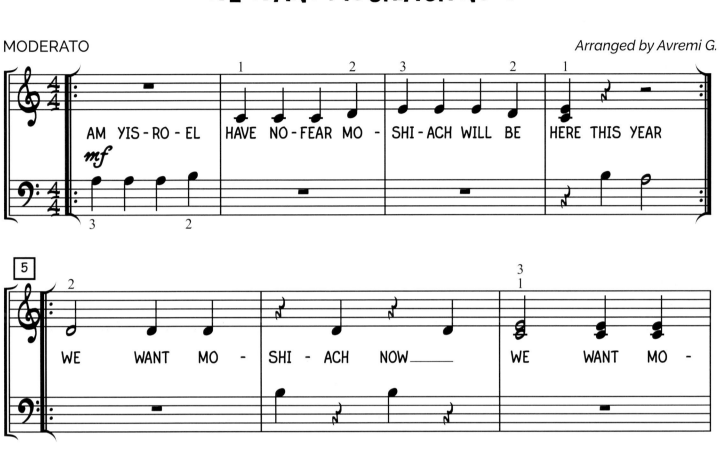

AM YIS-RO-EL HAVE NO-FEAR MO - SHI-ACH WILL BE HERE THIS YEAR

WE WANT MO - SHI - ACH NOW_____ WE WANT MO -

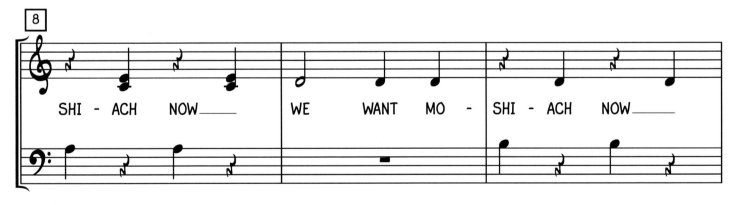

SHI - ACH NOW_____ WE WANT MO - SHI - ACH NOW_____

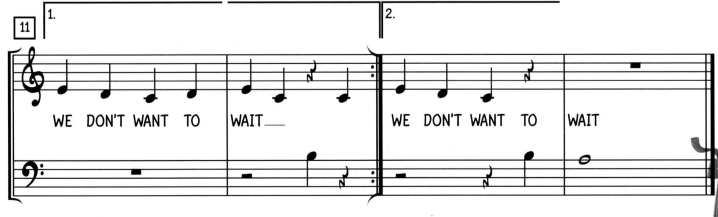

1.
WE DON'T WANT TO WAIT_____

2.
WE DON'T WANT TO WAIT

13

ACCOMPANIMENT

PROGRESS CHART	BEGINNING	PROGRESSING	MASTERED
STUDENT LEVEL 1			
ACCOMPANIMENT LEVEL 2			

Level 2

Student will practice alternating left and right hands in this song. Play with accompaniment to practice even rhythm. Thirds are introduced with the left hand.

DIDON NOTZACH

STUDENT PLAYS TWO OCTAVES HIGHER

MODERATO

Arranged by Avremi G.

Bass Clef C

In this song we introduce a new left hand position with the fifth finger on Low C.

DIDON NOTZACH

MODERATO

Arranged by Avremi G.

PROGRESS CHART	BEGINNING	PROGRESSING	MASTERED
STUDENT LEVEL 1			
ACCOMPANIMENT LEVEL 4			

Level 4
Student will practice shifting positions while switching from Finger 1 to Finger 2 in Measure 5 of this song.

MODEH ANI

STUDENT PLAYS TWO OCTAVES HIGHER

ALLEGRO

Arranged by Avremi G.

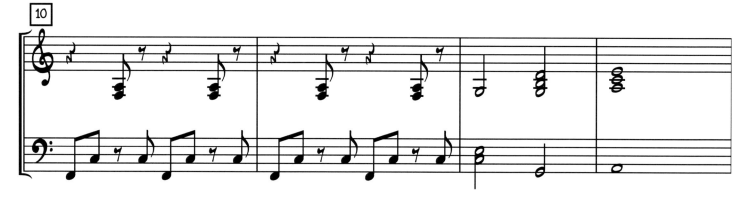

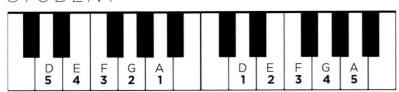

STUDENT

♪ NOTES

Two Positions

This song your right hand moves from C position to thumb on D.
Allegro means to play quickly, 109-132 BPM.

MODEH ANI

ALLEGRO

Arranged by Avremi G.

ACCOMPANIMENT

PROGRESS CHART	BEGINNING	PROGRESSING	MASTERED
STUDENT LEVEL 1			
ACCOMPANIMENT LEVEL 4			

Level 4

This Level 4 accompaniment has more advanced rhythm. Playing this accompaniment with the student is an enjoyable way to develop rhythm skills.

ALEF BET

STUDENT PLAYS TWO OCTAVES HIGHER

MODERATO

Arranged by Avremi G.

Practice playing eighth notes in this song.

ALEF BET

MODERATO

Arranged by Avremi G.

ACCOMPANIMENT

Level 3

Learn to play a dotted quarter note in this song.

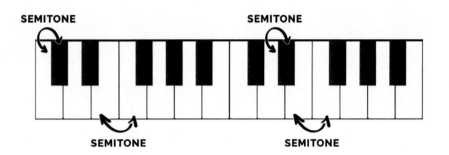

A **semitone** is a half step on the piano. A half step is moving from one piano key to the black or white key that is directly next to it.

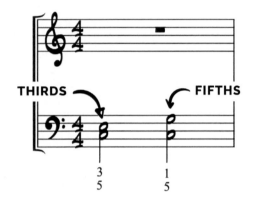

A **third** is two piano keys with a key in the middle.

A **major third** is four semitones.

A **minor third** is three semitones.

A **perfect fifth** is 7 semitones.

ASHER BORO

STUDENT PLAYS TWO OCTAVES HIGHER

Arranged by Avremi G.

MODERATO

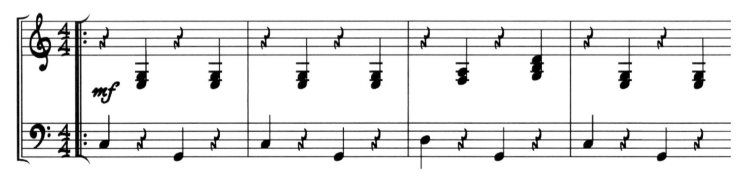

continued on Page 22

20

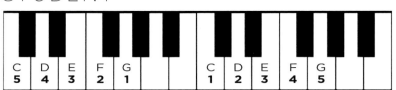

Use the following exercises to prepare for playing Asher Boro.

Practice Exercises

A **diad** is two notes played at the same time.

Practice playing thirds & fifths in this exercise.

Practice playing this rhythm before starting Asher Boro.

ASHER BORO

MODERATO

Arranged by Avremi G.

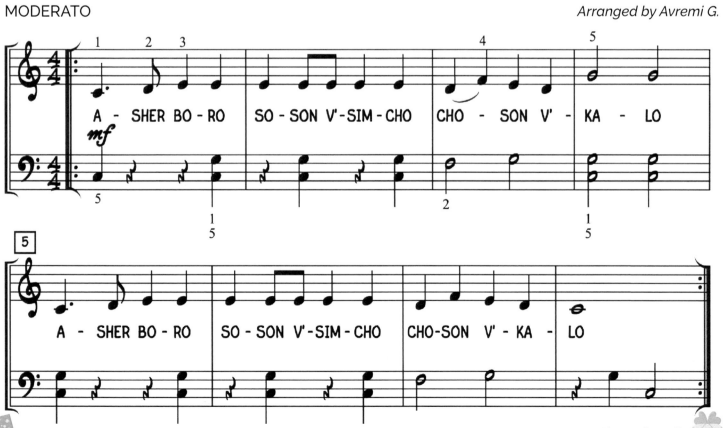

continued on Page 23

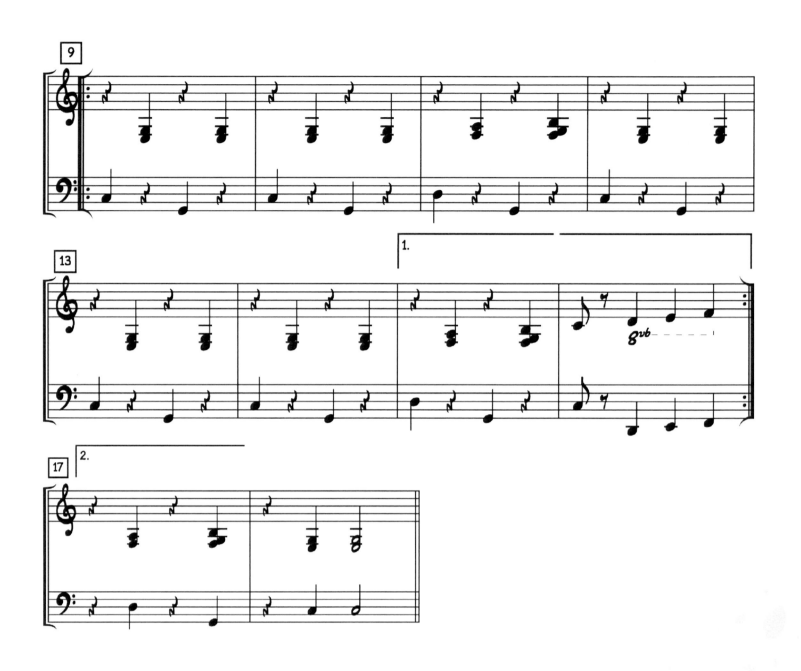

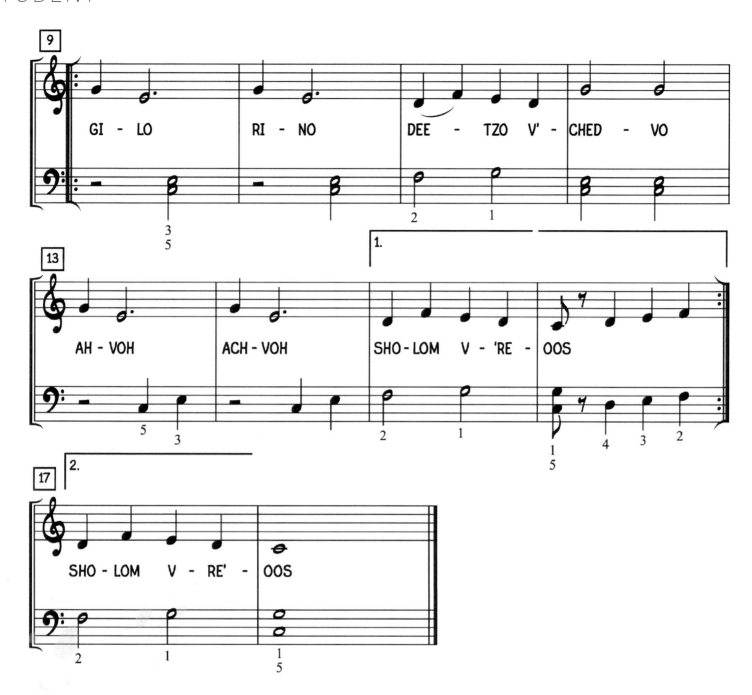

PIANO NOTATION WORKSHEET

MATCH THE TERMS WITH THEIR PARTNERS!

mp ●	● half step on the piano
f ●	● play quickly
ANDANTE ●	● (half note tie)
MODERATO ●	● mezzo forte: medium loud
ALLEGRO ●	● ♭
SLUR ●	● ♯
TIE ●	● piano: soft
REPEAT SIGN ●	● A relaxed slow tempo
SEMITONE ●	● 𝄆
SHARP ●	● forte: loud
FLAT ●	● moderate tempo
mf ●	● mezzo piano: medium soft
p ●	● (slur note)

NOTES

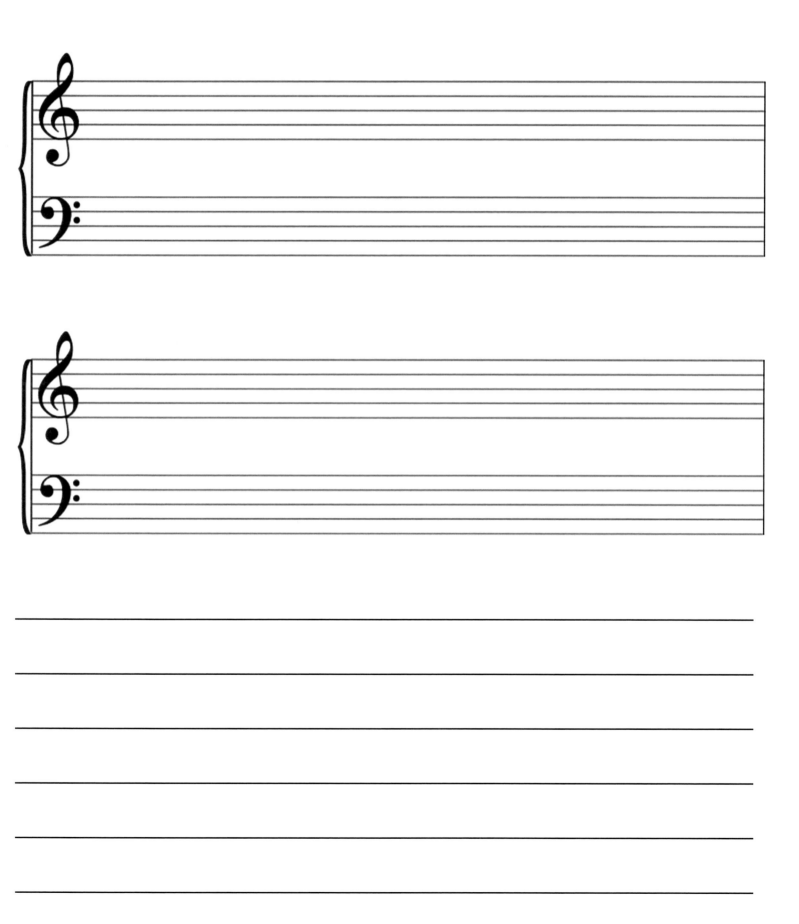

NOTES

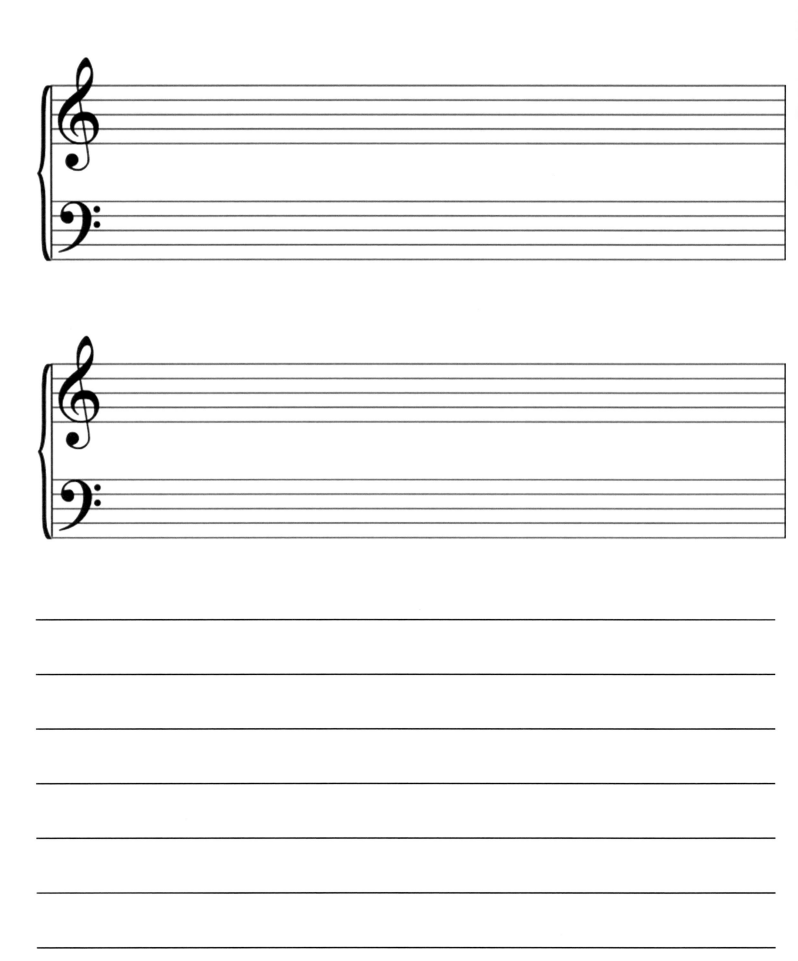

SIMON JEWISH MUSIC SERIES

CERTIFICATE OF COMPLETION

has successfully completed **Level 1** of the **Simon Jewish Music Series.** Congratulations! You are now ready to move on to **Level 2.**

_____
Piano Teacher

_____
Date